rockschool®

Acoustic Guitar
Grade 3

Performance pieces, technical exercises, supporting tests and in-depth guidance for Rockschool examinations

All accompanying and supporting audio can be downloaded from: *www.rslawards.com/downloads*

Input the following code when prompted: **3ZE5N4XJHG**

For more information, turn to page 5

Acknowledgements

Published by Rockschool Ltd. © 2016
Catalogue Number RSK200023
ISBN: 978-1-910975-30-5
13 October 2016 | Errata details can be found at *www.rslawards.com*

SYLLABUS
Syllabus written and devised by Nik Preston and Andy G Jones
Syllabus consultants: Carl Orr and James Betteridge
Arrangements by Andy G Jones, Carl Orr and James Betteridge
Supporting Tests written by Nik Preston and Andy G Jones
Syllabus advisors: Simon Troup and Jamie Humphries

PUBLISHING
Fact Files written by Diego Kovadloff
Music engraving and book layout by Simon Troup and Jennie Troup of Digital Music Art
Proof reading and copy editing by Diego Kovadloff, Carl Orr and Mary Keene
Cover design by Philip Millard
Cover photograph © Scott Gries/Getty Images

AUDIO
Produced by Nik Preston, Andy G Jones, Carl Orr and James Betteridge
Engineered by Andy G Jones, Carl Orr, James Betteridge, Jonas Persson and Music Sales
Mixed by Ash Preston, Andy G Jones, Carl Orr and James Betteridge
Mastered by Ash Preston and Paul Richardson
Supporting Tests recorded by Andy G Jones
Executive producers: John Simpson and Norton York

MUSICIANS
Andy G Jones, Carl Orr, James Betteridge, Nik Preston, Ian Thomas, Mike Finnigan, Noel McCalla,
Patti Revell, Hannah Vasanth and Jon Tatum

SPONSORSHIP
Andy G Jones endorses Thomastik Infeld strings, Providence cables and pedal switching systems, Free The Tone effects,
JJ Guitars, Ergoplay guitar supports and Wampler Pedals. All nylon strings parts recorded direct with the Yamaha NTX2000.
Carl Orr endorses MI Audio Revelation amps & effects, and Picato strings.
James Betteridge plays Martin guitars and D'addario strings.

DISTRIBUTION
Exclusive Distributors: Music Sales Ltd

CONTACTING ROCKSCHOOL
www.rslawards.com
Telephone: +44 (0)345 460 4747
Email: *info@rslawards.com*

Table of Contents

Introductions & Information

Rockschool Grade Pieces

Technical Exercises

Supporting Tests

Additional Information

Welcome to Rockschool Acoustic Guitar Grade 3

Welcome to **Rockschool's 2016 Acoustic Guitar syllabus**. This syllabus has been designed to equip all aspiring guitarists with a range of stylistically appropriate, industry relevant skills and a thoroughly engaging learning experience.

Utilising an array of well known repertoire and a truly crucial range of supporting tests, the continued progression of any student is assured from Debut through to Grade 8.

The syllabus has been authored to ensure that each student can develop as accompanists, soloists, sight readers and improvisers, whilst enabling both teacher and student to choose the areas that they wish to specialise in.

Rockschool's long standing commitment to raising academic standards, assessing industry-relevant skills and ensuring student engagement is world renowned. The 2016 Acoustic Guitar syllabus has been conceived in order to build upon this success and continue the evolution of the contemporary music world's first awarding body.

When combined with **Rockschool's 2015 Popular Music Theory syllabus**, this syllabus is guaranteed to furnish every candidate with both the practical skills and theoretical understanding necessary to perform at the highest level, across a whole range of contemporary repertoire.

Nik Preston – Head of Product Development and Publishing

Acoustic Guitar Exams

At each grade you have the option of taking one of two different types of examination:

- **Grade Exam**
  (Debut to Grade 5)
  A Grade Exam is a mixture of music performances, technical work and tests. You are required to prepare three pieces (two of which may be Free Choice Pieces) and the contents of the Technical Exercise section. This accounts for 75% of the exam marks. The other 25% consists of: either a Sight Reading or an Improvisation & Interpretation test (10%), two Ear Tests (10%), and finally you will be asked five General Musicianship Questions (5%). The pass mark is 60%.

  (Grades 6–8)
  A Grade Exam is a mixture of music performances, technical work and tests. You are required to prepare three pieces (two of which may be Free Choice Pieces) and the contents of the Technical Exercise section. This accounts for 75% of the exam marks. The other 25% consists of: a Quick Study Piece (10%), two Ear Tests (10%), and finally you will be asked five General Musicianship Questions (5%). The pass mark is 60%.

- **Performance Certificate**
  A Performance Certificate is equivalent to a Grade Exam, but in a Performance Certificate you are required to perform five pieces. A maximum of three of these can be Free Choice Pieces. Each song is marked out of 20 and the pass mark is 60%.

Book Contents

The book is divided into a number of sections:

- **Exam Pieces**
  Each exam piece is preceded by a Fact File detailing information about the original recording, the composer and the artist/s who performed it. There is also a Technical Guidance section at the end of each piece which provides insight from the arrangers as to the harmonic, melodic, rhythmic and technical nuance of each piece.

  Every exam piece is notated for acoustic guitar, but certain pieces feature two 'assessed' parts, meaning the candidate has the choice of which part they wish to perform in the exam. Certain pieces contain 'non-assessed' guitar parts, which are intended for duet/ensemble practice and performance. Likewise, certain pieces include notated vocal melodies in addition to the assessed guitar part. These have been included as reference material and to provide opportunity for duet and ensemble practice and performance. In your exam you must perform your pieces to the backing tracks provided.

- **Technical Exercises**
  There are either three or four types of technical exercise, depending on the grade:
  Group A – scales
  Group B – arpeggios/broken chords
  Group C – chord voicings
  Group D – a choice of stylistic studies. Please note, Group D only exists at Grades 6–8.

- **Supporting Tests**
  You are required to undertake three kinds of unprepared, supporting test:

  1. Sight Reading or an Improvisation & Interpretation test at Debut to Grade 5.
     Please note, these are replaced by mandatory Quick Study Pieces (QSPs) at Grades 6–8.

  2. Ear Tests: Debut to Grade 3 feature Melodic Recall and Chord Recognition.
     Grades 4–8 feature Melodic Recall and Harmonic Recall.

  3. General Musicianship Questions (GMQs), which you will be asked by the examiner at the end of each exam.
     Each book features examples of the types of unprepared tests likely to appear in the exam.
     The examiner will give you a different version in the exam.

- **General Information**
  You will find information on exam procedures, including online examination entry, marking schemes, information on Free Choice Pieces and improvisation requirements for each grade.

Audio
In addition to the Grade book, we have also provided audio in the form of backing tracks (minus assessed guitar part) and examples (including assessed guitar part) for both the pieces and the supporting tests where applicable. This can be downloaded from RSL directly at *www.rslawards.com/downloads*

You will need to input this code when prompted: **3ZE5N4XJHG**

The audio files are supplied in MP3 format. Once downloaded you will be able to play them on any compatible device.

You can find further details about Rockschool's Acoustic Guitar syllabus by downloading the syllabus guide from our website: *www.rslawards.com*

All candidates should download and read the accompanying syllabus guide when using this grade book.

Acoustic Guitar Notation Explained

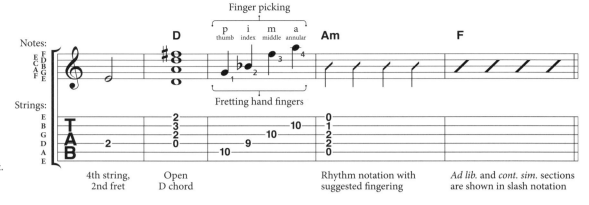

THE MUSICAL STAVE shows pitches and rhythms and is divided by lines into bars. Pitches are named after the first seven letters of the alphabet.

TABLATURE graphically represents the guitar fingerboard. Each horizontal line represents a string, and each number represents a fret.

4th string, 2nd fret | Open D chord | Rhythm notation with suggested fingering | *Ad lib.* and *cont. sim.* sections are shown in slash notation

Definitions For Special Guitar Notation

HAMMER ON: Pick the lower note, then sound the higher note by fretting it without picking.

PULL OFF: Pick the higher note then sound the lower note by lifting the finger without picking.

SLIDE: Pick the first note, then slide to the next with the same finger.

STRING BENDS: Pick the first note then bend (or release the bend) to the pitch indicated in brackets.

GLISSANDO: A small slide off of a note toward the end of its rhythmic duration. Do not slide 'into' the following note – subsequent notes should be repicked.

VIBRATO: Vibrate the note by bending and releasing the string smoothly and continuously.

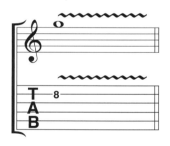

NATURAL HARMONICS: Lightly touch the string above the indicated fret then pick to sound a harmonic.

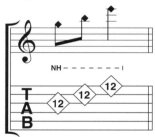

ARTIFICIAL HARMONICS: Fret the note indicated in the TAB, then (with picking hand lightly touch the string above fret indicated between staves, and pick to sound the harmo

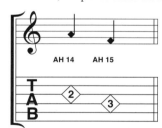

PRE-BENDS: Before picking the note, bend the string from the fret indicated between the staves, to the equivalent pitch indicated in brackets in the TAB

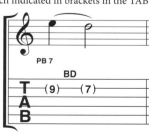

PICK HAND TAP: Strike the indicated note with a finger from the picking hand. Usually followed by a pull off.

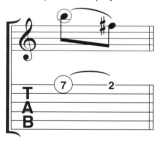

FRET HAND TAP: As pick hand tap, but use fretting hand. Usually followed by a pull off or hammer on.

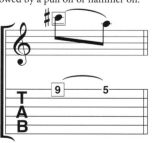

QUARTER TONE BEND: Pick the note indicated and bend the string up by a quarter tone.

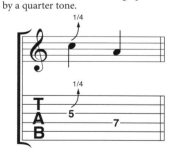

TRILL: Rapidly alternate between the two bracketed notes by hammering on and pulling off.

D.%. al Coda

- Go back to the sign (%), then play until the bar marked *To Coda* ⊕ then skip to the section marked ⊕ *Coda*.

D.C. al Fine

- Go back to the beginning of the song and play until the bar marked *Fine* (end).

- Repeat bars between signs.

- When a repeated section has different endings, play the first ending only the first time and the second ending only the second time.

Acoustic Guitar Grade 3

SONG TITLE: THINKING OUT LOUD

ALBUM: X / 2014

LABEL: ASYLUM / ATLANTIC

GENRE: POP

WRITTEN BY: ED SHEERAN AND

AMY WADGE

GUITAR: ED SHEERAN

PRODUCER: JAKE GOSLING

UK CHART PEAK: 1

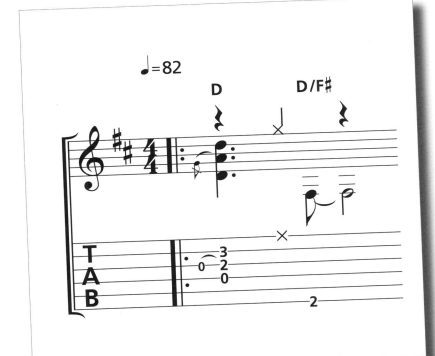

'Thinking Out Loud' was written by Ed Sheeran and Amy Wadge. The lyrics talk about everlasting love and are allegedly inspired by Sheeran's girlfriend at the time. The song is a romantic ballad with soul influences, particularly 'Let's Get It On' by Marvin Gaye.

'Thinking Out Loud' was released as a single and had phenomenal success worldwide, primarily through digital streaming. The video was viewed over 3/4 of a billion times on Youtube.

Ed Sheeran was born in West Yorkshire in 1991 and raised in Suffolk. He dropped out of school at 16 to pursue a career in music and moved to London. His independent releases caught the attention of Elton John and Jamie Foxx. He signed to Asylum Records in 2011.

In 2012 Sheeran made a guest appearance on Taylor Swift's Red and spent much of 2013 opening for her in the US. His second album release X reached number one in the UK and US charts.

Sheeran's early influences are Van Morrison, Bob Dylan, Eric Clapton and Damien Rice.

He is one of today's most commercially successful recording artists.

Thinking Out Loud

Ed Sheeran

Arranged by Andy G Jones

Thinking Out Loud | Technical Guidance

'Thinking Out Loud' by Ed Sheeran is a relatively simple tune with a I–IV–V harmonic movement reminiscent of Van Morrison.

The first inversion of the first chord D major adds movement with the F♯ bass leading smoothly into the G major chord. The electric guitar solo is included in the acoustic part as it is full of classic ideas. It is similar to Michael Landau's solo on Michael Buble's version of Van Morrison's 'Crazy Love', it is understated yet very effective, soulful and bluesy. The solo has many slides and some bends. If these are impossible due to a stiff action on your guitar, they could be changed to hammer-ons or slides.

The double stops on bar 35 are typical of soul guitar and very useful to any aspiring guitarist. The hammer on from A (5th) to B (6th) is typical of soul playing, from Curtis Mayfield onwards. The hammer on from D (root) to E (9th) is another idea worth incorporating to exploit in other contexts. The last idea in the solo, the diatonic double stops in bar 43, is also a classic approach heard in many styles, including Rockabilly. This phrase is delivered in triplets.

When Ed Sheeran plays rhythm he manages to hit the guitar on 2 and 4, many times managing to pick notes with his right hand at the same time as hitting the guitar or the guitar strings. This must be a legacy of his time spent playing solo as the percussive approach adds propulsion to the groove. Note that in bar 2 Sheeran uses the 9th (B) and the 6th (F♯) over an A major chord. This gives the pattern a soul or jazz feel. The descending bass line in bar 32 is harmonised also resembling Van Morrison's 'Crazy Love'.

Taylor Swift | Everything Has Changed

SONG TITLE: EVERYTHING HAS CHANGED

ALBUM: RED

LABEL: BIG MACHINE / REPUBLIC

GENRE: FOLK-POP

WRITTEN BY: TAYLOR SWIFT AND ED SHEERAN

GUITAR: ED SHEERAN

PRODUCER: BUTCH WALKER

UK CHART PEAK: 7

'Everything Has Changed' was written by Taylor Swift and Ed Sheeran. The song is featured on Taylor Swift's album *Red*. The lyrics are about the changes produced by the arrival of a new love. It was written in Taylor Swift's backyard and had a significant effect in exposing Ed Sheeran to US audiences.

Swift sang the song as a finale to her set during the Red tour and had Sheeran, who opened throughout the tour, joining her on stage.

Taylor Swift had a publishing contract prior to her debut album and composed over 250 songs including many collaborations. She refused to hand in much of her output to the publishers on the hope she was going to perform the songs herself. Things turned out as she wished and she now has a significant catalogue available to her.

Her style is influenced by Sheryl Crow and Brad Paisley amongst other country artists.

Swift is also a record producer and arranger and is involved in the developing of all the related artwork and packaging of her releases.

Everything Has Changed

Taylor Swift

Arranged by Carl Orr

Everything Has Changed | Technical Guidance

The first section of this song is essentially the classic I, VI, IV, V chord sequence used in countless songs since the middle of the last century. The bridge (bars 11–18) consists of G major (I/tonic), A minor (II/supertonic), C major (IV/subdominant) to D major (V/dominant) with a passing chord of E minor (VI/submediant) before the D major. The second section (bars 19–26) is a slight variation of the first section chords, with the D major (V) and C major (IV) chords reversed.

Although Ed Sheeran's propulsive acoustic guitar strumming drives this poignant song, the melody made for a more challenging exam piece, laced as it is, from start to finish, with the offbeat and subtle syncopations Sheeran is famous for. As the rhythms of the melody are intricate, it is important to clap each phrase before playing the notes. The melody can be broken down into 2–4 bar phrases for practice; bars 2–6, bars 7–10, bars 11–14, bars 15–16, bars 17–18, bars 19–22, bars 23–26, bars 27–30, bars 30–33. Once the rhythm is secure, the pitches can be learnt and applied to each phrase, eventually playing the whole melody.

As the melody is a harmonised duet, both vocal parts have been written out as an option. If you choose to play the melody without the harmony part, play the lower part from bars 15 to 18, and the upper part from bar 19.

The melody can be played with alternating up and down strokes as you see fit.

The harmony part, however, presents greater technical challenges. The double-stopped melody section from bars 15 to 18 can be played with index (i) and second (m) fingers and from bar 19 onwards with index finger (i) and third finger (a) through to the end.

However, it is also possible to play it with pick and fingers. It is important to figure out what is best for you, what sounds best and feels most natural.

This song is very challenging but rewarding and is a great technical study for sharpening up syncopated rhythms, and, if the harmonised melody is chosen, it is an excellent grounding in double-stops.

Foo Fighters | Best Of You

SONG TITLE: BEST OF YOU / 2005

ALBUM: IN YOUR HONOR

LABEL: RCA

GENRE: HARD ROCK

WRITTEN BY: DAVE GROHL

GUITAR: CHRIS SHIFLETT AND
DAVE GROHL

PRODUCER: NICK RASKULINECZ AND
FOO FIGHTERS

UK CHART PEAK: 4

'Best Of You' is featured on the Foo Fighter's fifth studio album, *In Your Honor*. It was also covered by Anastacia in 2012. The song was written by Dave Grohl after appearances at the 2004 presidential campaign trail with candidate John Kerry. Upon hearing that George Bush's campaign was using 'Times Like These', Grohl decided to lend his support to Kerry by playing 'Best Of You' for the campaign. The song was also performed at Live Earth in 2008.

Dave Grohl is a founder member of Nirvana and Foo Fighters is the name he chose for a one man project following the death of Kurt Cobain in 1994. Grohl eventually recruited other members and Foo Fighters became a band in 1995. The band has won four Grammys.

Grohl was already writing tunes during his Nirvana days but felt intimidated by Cobain's prowess. When the Foo Fighters started he borrowed elements from Nirvana's approach, such as the shift between quiet verses and loud choruses and the stripped down qualities of their songs. Grohl's riffs contain a substantial rhythmic element that relates to his drumming.

The band has developed a more sophisticated and melodic sound over the years. Grohl directed the series *Sonic Highways,* described as a 'love letter to the history of American music', in which much of what influences him and the Foo Fighters is documented.

Arranged by James Betteridge

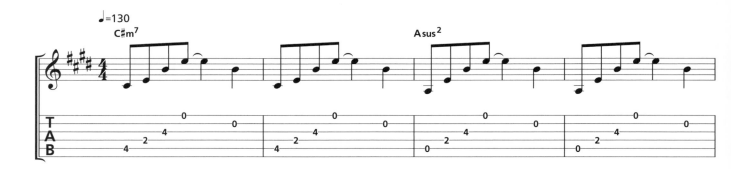

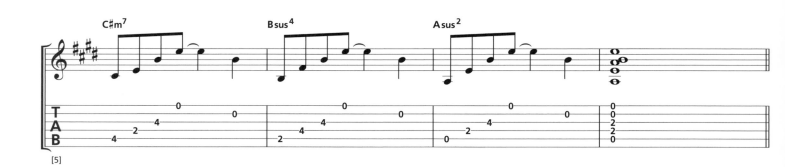

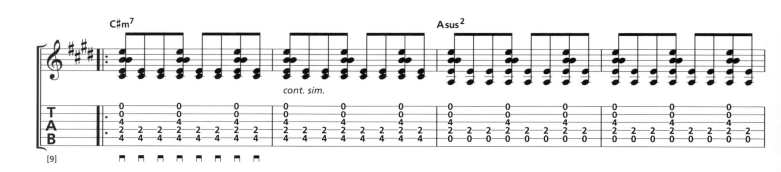

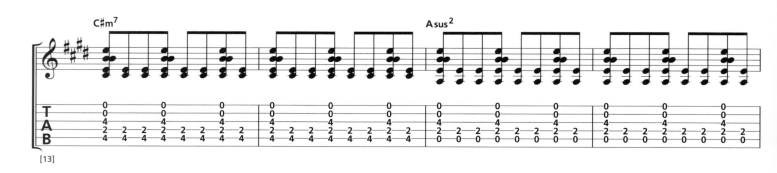

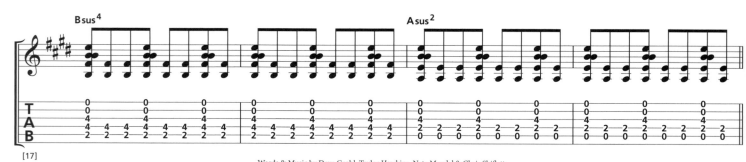

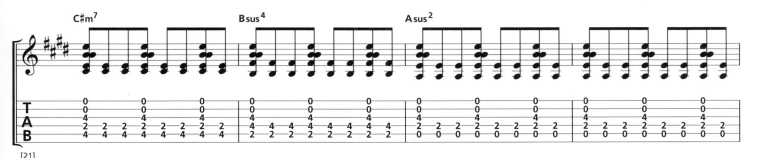

[21]

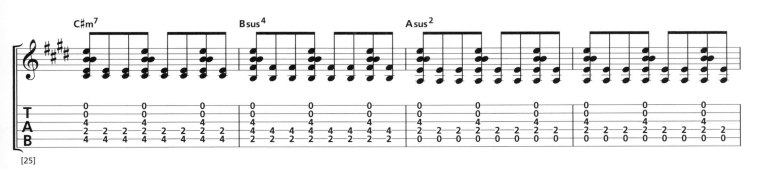

[25]

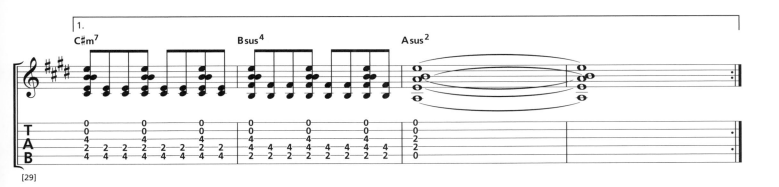

[29]

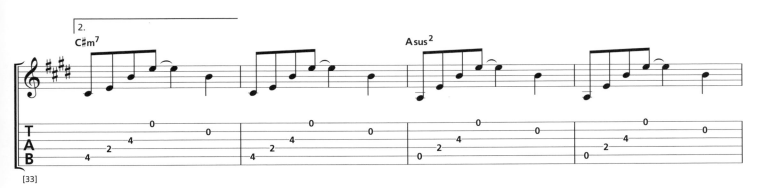

[33]

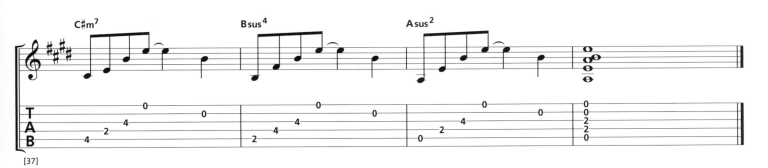

[37]

Best Of You | Technical Guidance

'Best Of You' is in the key of C# minor and is based around three diatonic chords – C#m^7 (I/tonic), A sus^2 (VI/submediant), and B sus^4 (VII/leading note). Sus chords, such as B sus^4, have the third replaced by the second or fourth, giving the sound a "suspended" quality.

The diagram below illustrates where these chords belong in the key.

The C# natural minor scale:

I	II	♭III	IV	V	♭VI	♭VII
C#m	D#dim	E maj	F#m	G#m	A maj	B maj
C#m					A maj	B maj

These chords can feel complex to begin with. The voicings featured involve using the open B and E strings to provide a drone effect that adds an unusual texture and colour to the overall sound.

The intro to the song is an arpeggiated pattern. Whilst this part is not on the original recording, it provides a good exercise in pick control. It is important to make sure all the notes are picked cleanly so they can be heard clearly.

The main rhythm is a driving 8th note pattern. It is advisable to use all down strokes for this part. This will add urgency to the sound. It might be useful to experiment using different gauge plectrums to produce an even sound across the strings. As a general rule, a thinner pick will help achieve this.

When practising the song, it is important to strive for accuracy first. If using a metronome, it is advisable to set it to a manageable tempo and only increase it once the parts are learnt.

Other alternative rock bands to listen to include Nirvana, Red Hot Chili Peppers, Radiohead, Coldplay and Muse. They all feature good examples of unusual and creative guitar playing.

It is important to use dynamic range and play harder during the chorus.

Aerosmith | I Don't Want To Miss A Thing

SONG TITLE: I DON'T WANT TO
MISS A THING

ALBUM: ARMAGEDDON SOUNDTRACK

LABEL: ASYLUM / ATLANTIC

GENRE: POP ROCK

WRITTEN BY: DIANE WARREN

GUITAR: JOE PERRY

PRODUCER: MATT SERLETIC

UK CHART PEAK: 4

'I Don't Want to Miss a Thing' debuted at number one in the US Billboard Hot 100 and was Aerosmith's first number one, after 28 years together. It was written by Diane Warren whose compositions have been covered by Whitney Houston, Toni Braxton, Michael Bolton and Bon Jovi amongst many others.

The song became a classic in the power ballad genre and exposed Aerosmith to a new generation of fans.

Aerosmith formed in Boston, Massachusetts, in 1970. Their brand of hard rock has incorporated elements of pop, heavy metal and rhythm and blues. Their song 'Walk This Way' was covered by Run DMC in 1987 and became a classic in the then new rap rock genre.

Aerosmith have sold over 150 million records and are the epitome of a bad boy rock band, with Steven Tyler, their frontman, already an iconic wild child. In 2013 Tyler and guitarist Joe Perry were inducted into the Songwriters Hall of Fame. Aerosmith's sound was influential to 1980's bands such as Van Halen, Motley Crew and Guns N' Roses. The band has released 15 albums to date. The game *Guitar Hero: Aerosmith* was released in 2008. Joe Perry is acknowledged as a legendary lead guitarist in the genre.

I Don't Want To Miss A Thing

Aerosmith

Arranged by James Betteridge

[5]

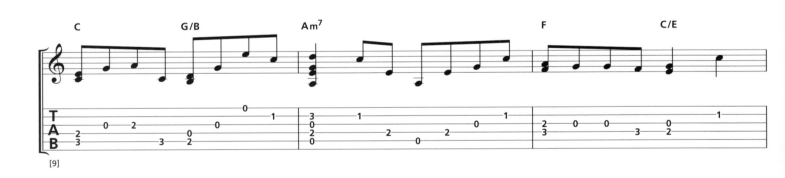

[9]

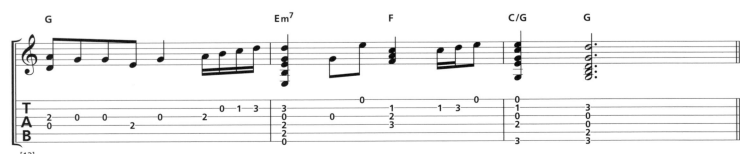

[12]

Words & Music by Diane Warren
© Copyright 1998 Realsongs.
Universal/MCA Music Limited.
All Rights Reserved. International Copyright Secured.

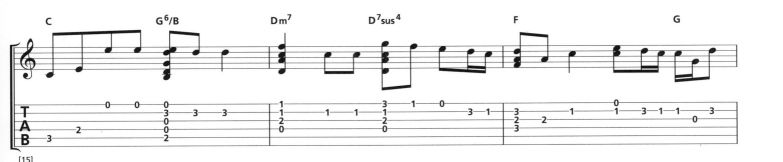

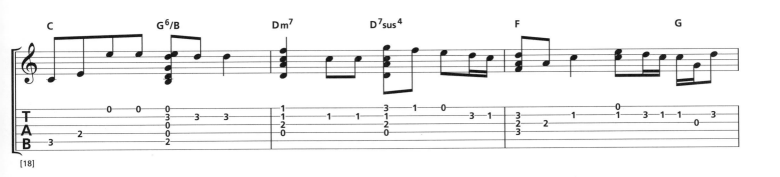

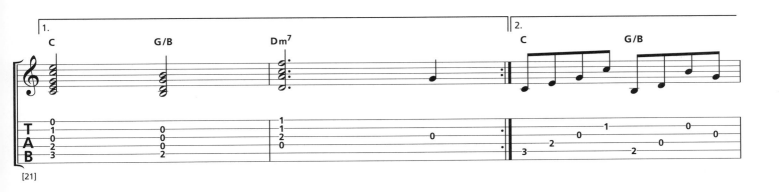

I Don't Want To Miss A Thing | Technical Guidance

This abridged arrangement of ' I Don't Want To Miss A Thing' is based around a verse and chorus of the song. It is in the key of C major and uses the C major (I/tonic), F major (IV/subdominant), G major (V/dominant), A minor (VIm/submediant) and D minor (IIm/supertonic) chords.

The C major scale:

I	II	III	IV	V	VI	VII
C maj	Dm	Em	F maj	G maj	Am	B dim
C maj	Dm		F maj	G maj	Am	

The song starts with an 8th note arpeggiated pattern that outlines C major, G major, A minor^7 and F major. For this section the focus should be on trying to achieve an even sound. It is important to avoid unwanted open strings.

Both sections involve playing the melody interspersed with chord fragments to provide the harmony. The melody is based around the notes from the C major scale, and contains some tricky 16th note rhythmic passages. Some chord names in this arrangement might be unfamiliar. For example, G/B is a first inversion of a G major triad. This simply means that the notes of the G chord have been arranged so that the B (third of the chord) is the lowest sounding note in it.

Difficult passages should be slowed down to a comfortable tempo during practice, striving for accuracy first. It is advisable to practice playing the chords and the melody separately to begin with.

For finger style playing, it would useful to remember these simple general guidelines:

- Let the thumb play the lowest note in the chord.
- If there is more than one note being played on a string, avoid using the same right hand finger twice.

To play along with the original recording, which is in the key of D major, a capo on the second fret should be utilised. The chord shapes will remain the same.

Alison Krauss | When You Say Nothing At All

SONG TITLE: WHEN YOU SAY
NOTHING AT ALL
ALBUM: KEITH WHITLEY: A
TRIBUTE ALBUM /
NOW THAT I'VE FOUND YOU:
A COLLECTION
LABEL: BNA
GENRE: COUNTRY
WRITTEN BY: PAUL OVERSTREET AND
DON SCHLITZ
GUITAR: RON BLOCK
PRODUCER: ALISON KRAUSS AND UNION
STATION
UK CHART PEAK: 91

'When You Say Nothing at All' was written by Paul Overstreet and Don Schlitz in the 1980's and covered by many artists since. Most notably Keith Whitley, Alison Krauss and Ronan Keating. Allegedly, the song was written at the end of an otherwise unproductive day and neither of the writers regarded it as a significant tune. It was Keith Whitley who, upon hearing it, decided to cover it.

Alison Krauss and Union Station recorded their version for a tribute album to Keith Whitley. The song was later featured in Krauss' *Now That I've Found You: A Collection* and peaked at number three in the Billboard Country Singles Chart.

Alison Krauss has had a remarkable career, spanning 25 years, although she is only 39.

Her songs are introspective and highly crafted. She blends tradition and topical themes very effectively. She has an experimental approach to writing and recording and her view is that what she sings needs to touch a deep emotional chord, whether written by herself or not. She works with renowned band Union Station, with whom she delivers an austere yet poignant sound, supported by exceptional musicianship.

Alison Krauss has received 26 Grammy awards. She has also collaborated with Robert Plant (Led Zeppelin's singer) on the critically acclaimed *Raising Sand*.

When You Say Nothing At All

Alison Krauss

Arranged by Andy G Jones

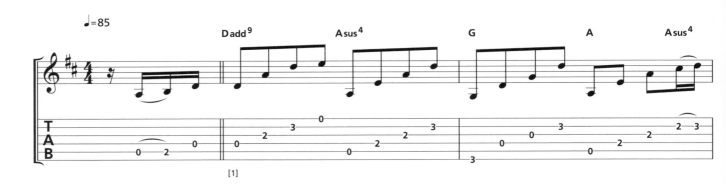

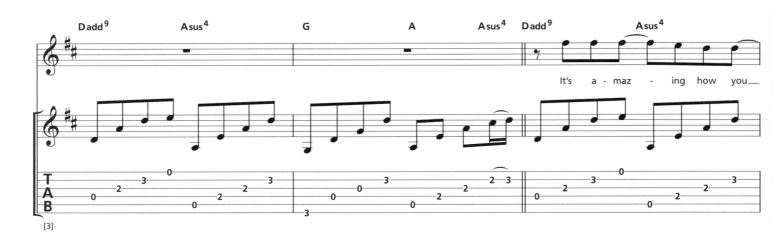

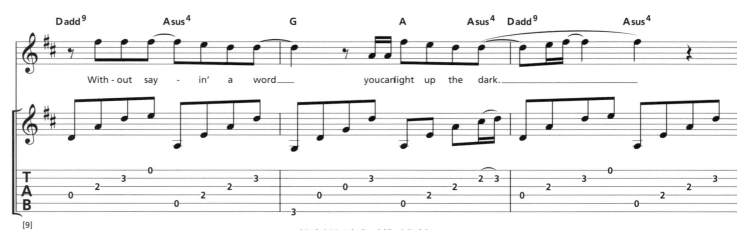

Words & Music by Don Schlitz & Paul Overstreet

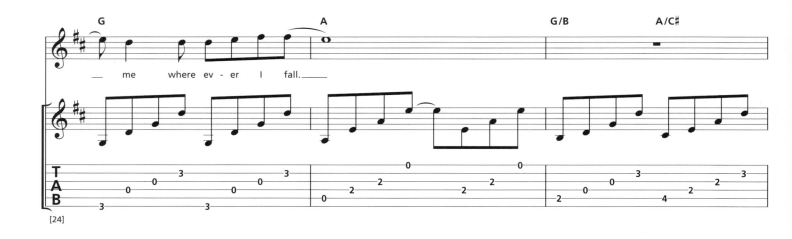

me where ev - er I fall.

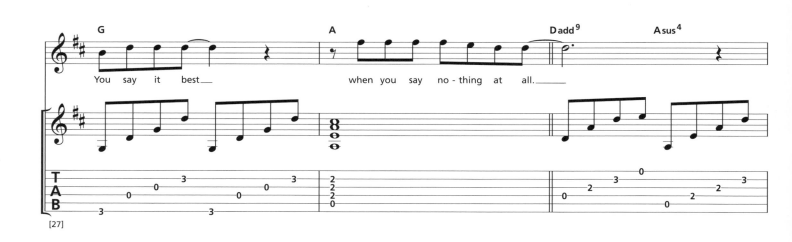

You say it best____ when you say no - thing at all._

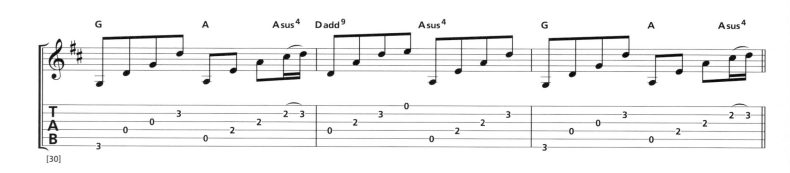

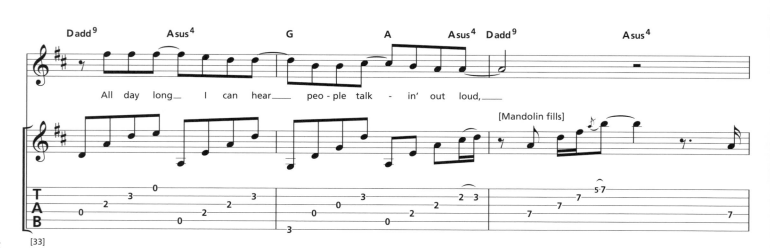

All day long____ I can hear____ peo - ple talk - in' out loud,_

[Mandolin fills]

When You Say Nothing At All | Technical Guidance

This adaptation of 'When You Say Nothing At All' has its roots in Alison Krauss' classy version. Her band Union Station are masterful musicians. Jerry Douglas is considered one of the finest dobro players and he heralded the modern approach to the instrument. Both guitarists in the band are outstanding players.

At first glance the accompaniment is very simple. However, sometimes it's the simple stuff that is the hardest to play well. Note the frequent use of the added 9th degree to the D and G major voicings. The 4th degree is used to spice up the A major chord (V). These details add character to the harmony.

Some details from the mandolin part on Krauss' recorded version are incorporated in this arrangement. See bars 35–36 for a typical mandolin style fill. This enhances the country feel of the piece.

Rascal Flatts | Bless The Broken Road

SONG TITLE: BLESS THE BROKEN ROAD
ALBUM: FEELS LIKE TODAY
LABEL: LYRIC STREET
GENRE: COUNTRY
WRITTEN BY: MARCUS HOMMON,
BOBBY BOYD AND
JEFF HANNA
GUITAR: JOE DON ROONEY
PRODUCER: MARK BRIGHT AND
MARTY WILLIAMS
UK CHART PEAK: 41

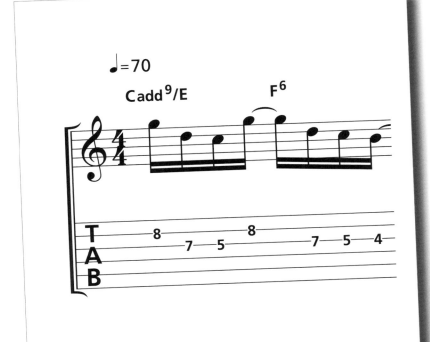

'Bless The Broken Road' was featured in Rascal Flatts' *Feels Like Today* album, released in 2004. The song was written ten years earlier by Marcus Hommon, Bobby Boyd and Jeff Hanna and covered by many artists since. The Rascal Flatts' version spent five weeks at number one in the Hot Country Singles and Tracks Chart. It was also awarded a Grammy for Best Country Song. The single sold over three million copies in the US. An acoustic version of the song was included in the soundtrack to *Hannah Montana: The Movie*.

Rascal Flatts formed in the year 2000 in Nashville. They quickly received attention and were given a record deal. They have sold over 22 million records to date and have included new generation artists such as Taylor Swift and Blake Shelton as opening acts to their shows. They are a modern country phenomenon. The band has received many awards in the country music field including membership of the Grand Ole Opry.

Their legendary shows are a state of the art extravaganza playing to sold out audiences across the US.

Rascal Flats are committed to giving back and are known for their charitable work.

Bless The Broken Road

Rascal Flatts

Arranged by Andy G Jones

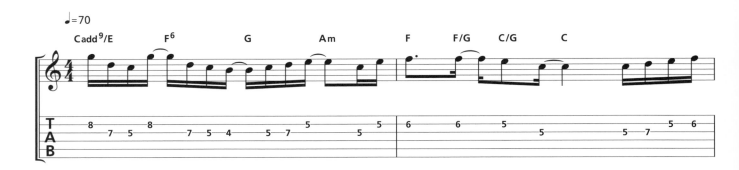

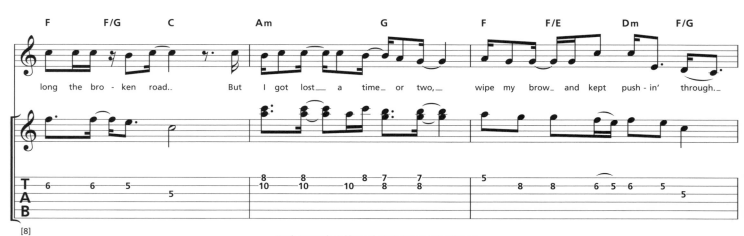

Words & Music by Bobby Boyd, Marcus Hummon & Jeff Hanna
© Copyright 1994 Jeff Diggs Music Limited/Careers BMG Music Publishing.
Bug Music Limited/Universal Music Publishing International MGB Limited.
All Rights Reserved. International Copyright Secured.

Bless The Broken Road | Technical Guidance

The parts on the original 'Bless The Broken Road' recording are a master class in good taste in the modern country rock style.

This version takes elements from the guitar, mandolin and piano parts to create constant melodic interest. The electric guitar solo from Rascal Flatts' recording has been adapted for our acoustic setting. If any of the detailed articulation is tricky, it is advisable to practise slowly and be very deliberate about fingering. Many of the melodic lines in this part could have been played lower. Tablature in the middle register is included so it is easier to transpose any ideas for use in other tunes.

Hybrid picking or fingerstyle can be used to execute this piece. Note that the solo was probably played with a pick. Some of the chordal and arpeggio based figures would be inappropriate for flat picking (using a pick only).

The harmony in this piece is peppered with chord inversions.

The chords in bar 2 demonstrate a common technique taken from gospel music. The F/G chord is followed by a C/G chord. F is a perfect 4th above C and this is called 'back cycling'. In many gospel influenced tunes, these chords would have been followed by a G^7 chord before hitting C major.

Technical Exercises

In this section, you will be asked to play a selection of exercises, chosen by the examiner, from each of the groups below.

All exercises need to be played:
- In the keys, octaves and tempos shown.
- In either swung or straight feel, as directed by the examiner.

You can use your book in the exam for Groups A and B. Group C must be performed from memory.

Note that Groups A and B need to be played to a click and any fingerings shown are suggestions only.

Group A: Scales
The tempo for this group is ♩=80 bpm.

1. A major scale

2. A major scale

3. E♭ major scale

4. E♭ major scale

Technical Exercises

5. F# natural minor scale

6. C natural minor scale

7. F# harmonic minor scale

8. C harmonic minor scale

9. C lydian scale

10. Chromatic scale on A | Ascending

11. Chromatic scale on A | Descending

12. Chromatic scale on E♭ | Ascending

13. Chromatic scale on E♭ | Descending

Group B: Arpeggios
The tempo for this group is ♩=69 bpm.

1. A major arpeggio

2. E♭ major arpeggio

3. F♯ minor arpeggio

4. C minor arpeggio

5. C major 7 (Cmaj⁷) arpeggio

6. C major 9♯11 (Cmaj⁹♯¹¹) arpeggio

7. C major 13♯11 (Cmaj¹³♯¹¹) arpeggio

Group C: Chord Voicings

In the exam you will be asked to play, from memory, your choice of one chord voicing from each of the following exercises, without the aid of a backing track or metronome. However, for practice purposes a demonstration of the chords played to a metronome click is available in the downloadable audio.

1. C major 7 (Cmaj^7)

2. C dominant 9 sus 4 (C^{9}sus^4)

Sight Reading

In this section you have a choice between either a sight reading test or an improvisation and interpretation test (see facing page).

The examiner will ask you which one you wish to choose before commencing. Once you have decided you cannot change your mind.

In the sight reading test, the examiner will give you a 4–8 bar melody in the key of E♭ major or A major. You will first be given 90 seconds to practise, after which the examiner will play the backing track twice. The first time is for you to practise and the second time is for you to perform the final version for the exam. For each playthrough, the backing track will begin with a one bar count-in. The tempo is ♩=60–95.

During the practice time, you will be given the choice of a metronome click throughout or a one bar count-in at the beginning.

The backing track is continuous, so once the first playthrough has finished, the count-in of the second playing will start immediately.

Sight Reading | Example 1

Please note: The test shown is an example. The examiner will give you a different version in the exam.

Sight Reading | Example 2

Please note: The test shown is an example. The examiner will give you a different version in the exam.

Improvisation & Interpretation

In the improvisation and interpretation test, the examiner will give you a 4–8 bar chord progression in the key of E♭ major or A major. You will first be given 90 seconds to practise, after which the examiner will play the backing track twice. The first time is for you to practise and the second time is for you to perform the final version for the exam. For each playthrough, the backing track will begin with a one bar count-in. The tempo is ♩ = 60–95.

During the practice time, you will be given the choice of a metronome click throughout or a one bar count-in at the beginning.

The backing track is continuous, so once the first playthrough has finished, the count-in of the second playing will start immediately.

You are only required to improvise single note melodies.

Improvisation & Interpretation | Example 1

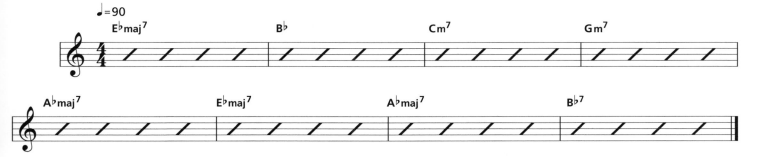

Please note: The test shown is an example. The examiner will give you a different version in the exam.

Improvisation & Interpretation | Example 2

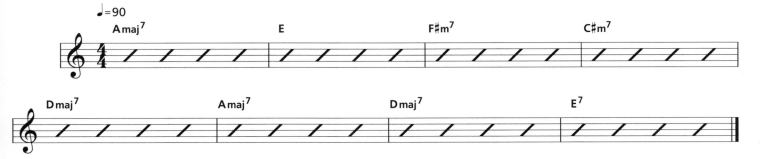

Please note: The test shown is an example. The examiner will give you a different version in the exam.

Ear Tests

In this section, there are two ear tests:
- Melodic Recall
- Chord Recognition

You will find one example of each type of test printed below and you will need perform both of them in the exam.

Test 1: Melodic Recall

The examiner will play you a 2 bar diatonic melody in the key of C major with a range up to a fifth. The first note will be the root note. You will hear the test twice, each time with a one bar count-in, then you will hear a further one bar count-in after which you will need to play the melody to the click. The tempo is ♩ = 95 bpm.

It is acceptable to play over the track as it is being played as well as practising after the second playthough. The length of time available after the second playthrough is pre-recorded on the audio track so the count-in may begin while you are still practising.

Please note: The test shown is an example. The examiner will give you a different version in the exam.

Test 2: Chord Recognition

The examiner will play you a sequence of chords, each with a C root note. You will hear the chord sequence twice, each time with a one bar count-in. You will then be asked to identify the chord quality of two of the chords, from a choice of major, minor, diminished, augmented, dominant 7th and major 7th. The tempo is ♩ = 95 bpm.

Please note: The test shown is an example. The examiner will give you a different version in the exam.

General Musicianship Questions

The final part of your exam is the General Musicianship Questions section, which features 5 questions relating to one of your choice of the performance pieces.

1. You will be asked a question relating to the harmony from a section of one of your pieces.

2. You will be asked a question relating to the melody in a section of one of your pieces.

3. You will be asked a question relating to the rhythms used in a section of one of your pieces.

4. You will be asked a question relating to the technical requirements of one of your pieces.

5. You will be asked a question relating to the genre of one of your pieces.

Entering Rockschool Exams

Entering a Rockschool exam is easy, just go online and follow our simple six step process. All details for entering online, dates, fees, regulations and Free Choice pieces can be found at *www.rslawards.com*

- All candidates should ensure they bring their own Grade syllabus book to the exam or have proof of digital purchase ready to show the examiner.

- All Grade 6–8 candidates must ensure that they bring valid photo ID to their exam.

Marking Schemes

Grade Exams | Debut to Grade 5 *

ELEMENT	PASS	MERIT	DISTINCTION
Performance Piece 1	12–14 out of 20	15–17 out of 20	18+ out of 20
Performance Piece 2	12–14 out of 20	15–17 out of 20	18+ out of 20
Performance Piece 3	12–14 out of 20	15–17 out of 20	18+ out of 20
Technical Exercises	9–10 out of 15	11–12 out of 15	13+ out of 15
Sight Reading *or* Improvisation & Interpretation	6 out of 10	7–8 out of 10	9+ out of 10
Ear Tests	6 out of 10	7–8 out of 10	9+ out of 10
General Musicianship Questions	3 out of 5	4 out of 5	5 out of 5
TOTAL MARKS	**60%+**	**74%+**	**90%+**

Grade Exams | Grades 6–8

ELEMENT	PASS	MERIT	DISTINCTION
Performance Piece 1	12–14 out of 20	15–17 out of 20	18+ out of 20
Performance Piece 2	12–14 out of 20	15–17 out of 20	18+ out of 20
Performance Piece 3	12–14 out of 20	15–17 out of 20	18+ out of 20
Technical Exercises	9–10 out of 15	11–12 out of 15	13+ out of 15
Quick Study Piece	6 out of 10	7–8 out of 10	9+ out of 10
Ear Tests	6 out of 10	7–8 out of 10	9+ out of 10
General Musicianship Questions	3 out of 5	4 out of 5	5 out of 5
TOTAL MARKS	**60%+**	**74%+**	**90%+**

Performance Certificates | Debut to Grade 8 *

ELEMENT	PASS	MERIT	DISTINCTION
Performance Piece 1	12–14 out of 20	15–17 out of 20	18+ out of 20
Performance Piece 2	12–14 out of 20	15–17 out of 20	18+ out of 20
Performance Piece 3	12–14 out of 20	15–17 out of 20	18+ out of 20
Performance Piece 4	12–14 out of 20	15–17 out of 20	18+ out of 20
Performance Piece 5	12–14 out of 20	15–17 out of 20	18+ out of 20
TOTAL MARKS	**60%+**	**75%+**	**90%+**

* Note that there are no Debut Vocal exams.

Copyright Information

Best Of You
(Grohl/Mendel/Hawkins/Shiflett)
Universal/MCA Music Limited/Bug Music Ltd

Thinking Out Loud
(Sheeran/Wadge)
BDI Music Limited/Sony/ATV Music Publishing (UK) Limited

I Don't Want to Miss A Thing
(Warren)
Universal/MCA Music Limited

When You Say Nothing At All
(Overstreet/Schlitz)
Screen Gems EMI Music Ltd/Universal/MCA Music Limited/Kobalt Music Publishing Limited

Everything Has Changed
(Swift/Sheeran)
Sony/ATV Music Publishing (UK) Limited

Bless The Broken Road
(Hanna/Boyd/Hummon)
Bug Music Ltd/Universal Music Publishing MGB Limited

mcps

rockschool®

DIGITAL DOWNLOADS NOW AVAILABLE!

All your favourite Rockschool titles are now available to download instantly from the RSL shop. Download entire grade books, individual tracks or supporting tests to all your devices.

START DOWNLOADING NOW

www.rslawards.com/shop